GW00859377

Terrance the Triceratops

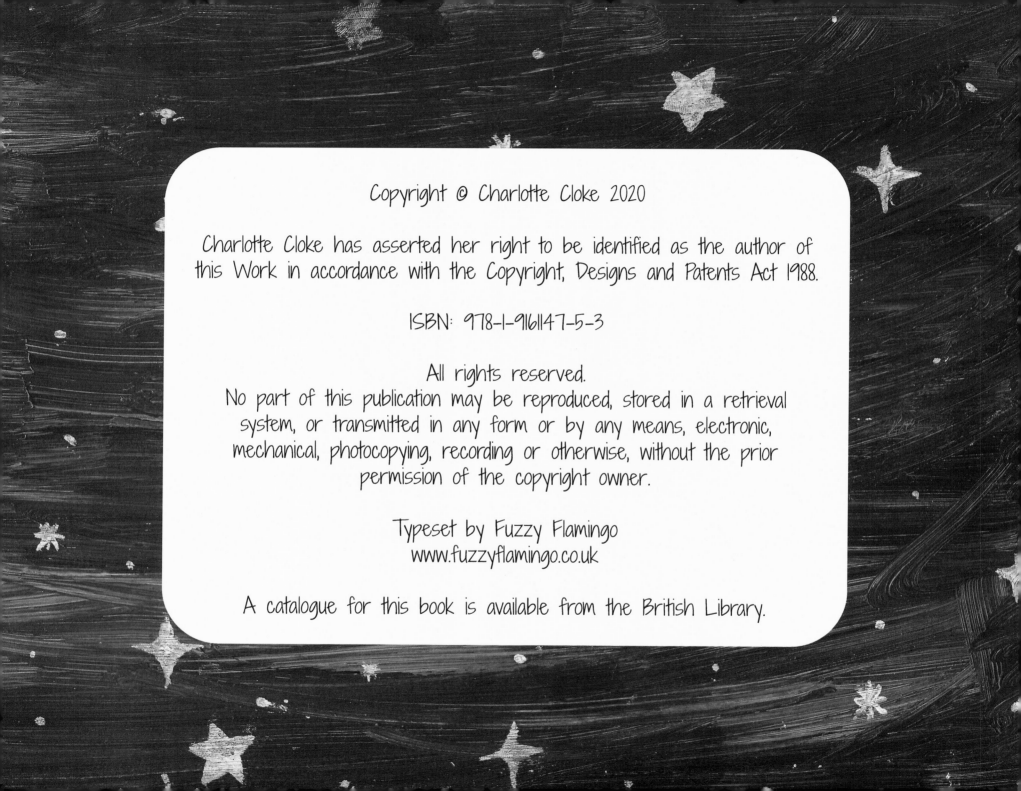

Copyright © Charlotte Cloke 2020

Charlotte Cloke has asserted her right to be identified as the author of this Work in accordance with the Copyright, Designs and Patents Act 1988.

ISBN: 978-1-9161147-5-3

All rights reserved.
No part of this publication may be reproduced, stored in a retrieval system, or transmitted in any form or by any means, electronic, mechanical, photocopying, recording or otherwise, without the prior permission of the copyright owner.

Typeset by Fuzzy Flamingo
www.fuzzyflamingo.co.uk

A catalogue for this book is available from the British Library.

To my wonderful
Eliott and Edith.
May you always
know how much
Mummy loves you. x

When Rex came upon his friend,
he was all of a dismay.

"My head's a terrible mess,"
he said, "and it has been all day."

Rex was beside himself,
he wasn't sure what to do.

He was sure their good friend Perry
would stop Terrance feeling so blue.

Perry the pterodactyl was flying overhead,
when all of Terrance's thoughts were high in the sky,
And he should have been sleeping in bed.

Perry heard each thought aloud,
and wondered what Terrance had been through,
what had made poor Terrance worry so much
and feel so rubbish too.

"There must be something we can do," he sighed.

Rex was wandering around the grounds,
Thinking up some more.
He heard a SWISH SWISH
so he looked up and saw...

Perry the pterodactyl,
flying up above.
Perry shouted down to Rex,
Terrance needs some love!

Perry and Rex thought long and hard,
they needed some help.
Perry saw the volcano
and an idea ERUPTED out of him!

"I'll fly and talk to Stan the stegosaurus
and Dave the diplodocus
and see if they have any ideas
to cheer poor Terrance up!"

Perry explained to Stan
and Stan knew what to do.
"Music," he said will cheer him up,
"Can you do the boogie boo?"

Perry kept on flying
for he wasn't sure that was it.
Maybe Dave the diplodocus
had an idea with the right fit.

Perry explained again
and Dave was excited.
He said what always cheered him
up was to sing the loopdy loo.

Perry said, "Thanks but no,
Terrance is sad and that won't do.

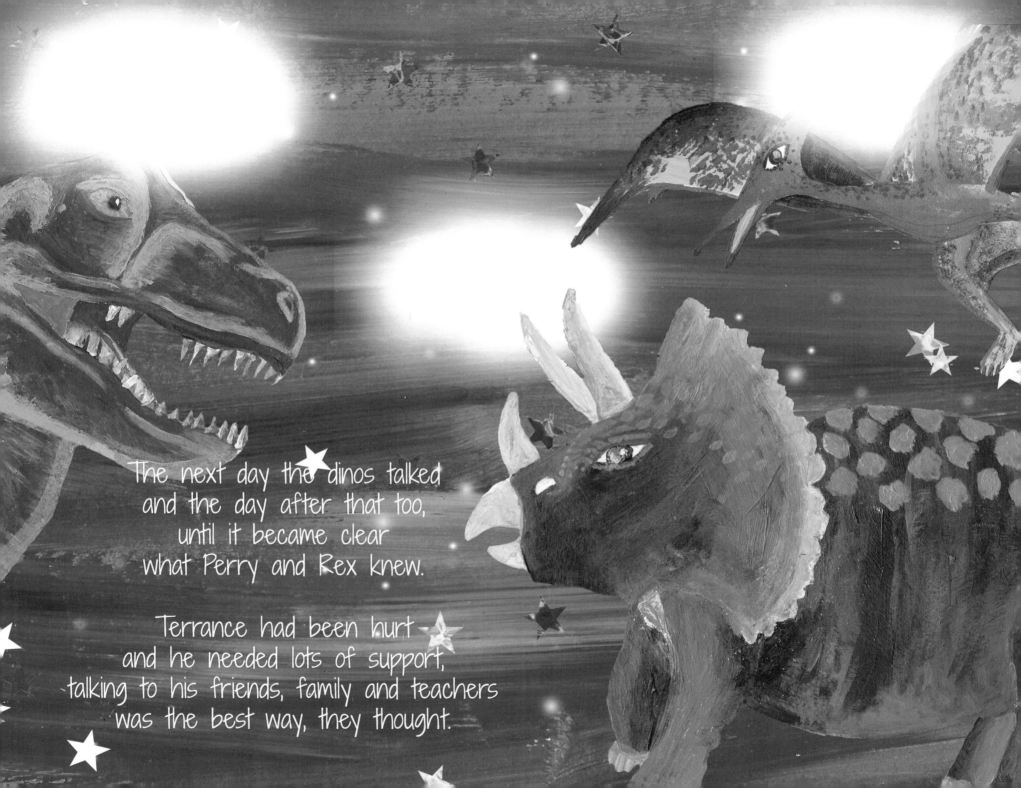

The next day the dinos talked
and the day after that too,
until it became clear
what Perry and Rex knew.

Terrance had been hurt
and he needed lots of support,
talking to his friends, family and teachers
was the best way, they thought.

Terrance they said, "It's never okay,
no matter who they are
or if they've had a bad day
for someone to hurt you
or say bad things
to make you feel a terrible way."

And so, Terrance
looked happier,
and felt happier too.
What wonderful
friends he had
to stop him feeling blue.

And remember this when you go to bed tonight.

When it feels like it'll always be dark,
know that the sun will come up in the morning,
no matter how dark or bad of a day.

With Thanks To:

My grandad, for believing in me, and our
cups of tea and Facetimes;
and my amazing partner, Neil, who gave
me a future to look forward to and offers
continuous support;
and my friends Clo and Jo, who have
been a shoulder when I've needed.

I love you all so very much! Thank you
for being amazing!

Lightning Source UK Ltd.
Milton Keynes UK
UKRC011357120620
364902UK00005B/117